CAPTAIN PUGWASH

in

The Battle of Bunkum Bay

A Cartoon Story
by
JOHN RYAN

PUFFIN BOOKS

French Fleet

Flying
Dustm

The UNION JACK at the time of this story was as it is today, except that the red diagonal cross of St. Patrick had not been added. So there was no "right" and "wrong" way up.

THE BATTLE OF BUNKUM BAY

A Map of the PAJAMAH ISLANDS showing BUNKUM BAY where the SPANISH BULLION SHIP was lost, the advance of the BRITISH and FRENCH NAVIES & the HEROIC INTERVENTION intended by CAPTAIN HORATIO PUGWASH.

British Fleet

The FRENCH had a different flag to that used today. It was either white, or sometimes blue, with three golden "fleur-de-lys" as shown in this story.

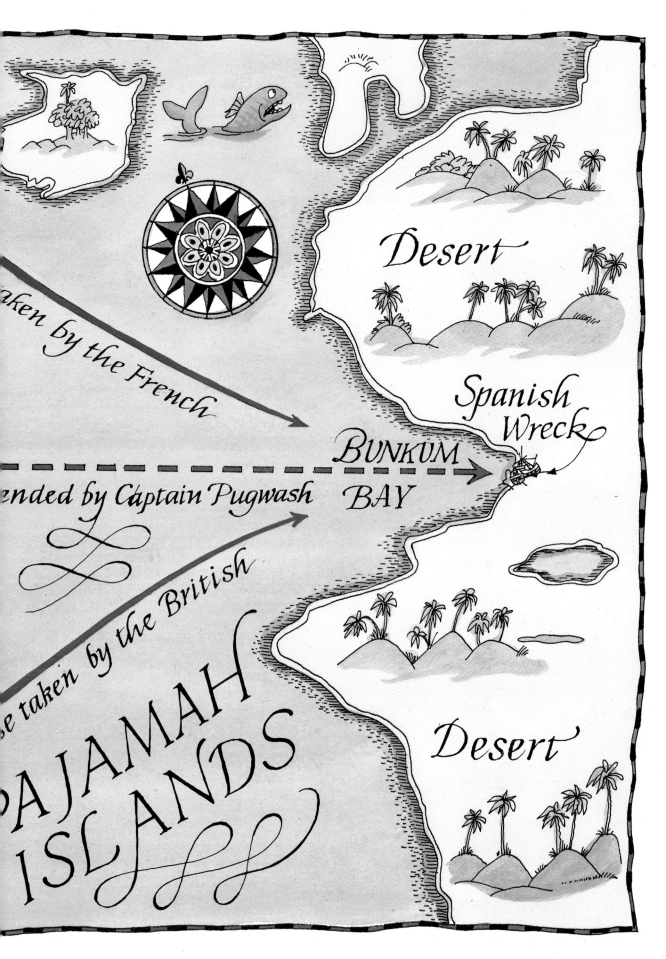

CAPTAIN PUGWASH

The Battle of Bunkum Bay
by John Ryan

OF ALL THE GREAT NAVAL ENCOUNTERS BETWEEN THE FRENCH & THE BRITISH, NONE SHOULD BE MORE FAMOUS THAN THE BATTLE OF BUNKUM BAY, AND YET, UNTIL NOW, ITS STORY HAS NEVER BEEN TOLD...

 ... BOTH PIGEONS STOPPED OFF ON THEIR WAY TO SEE AN OLD FRIEND OF THEIRS, CABIN BOY TOM, WHO SERVED ON CAPTAIN PUGWASH'S SHIP THE Black Pig, WHICH WAS ALSO IN THE ISLANDS.

Bunkum Bay? But that's quite close!

TOM FED THEM, SHOWED THEIR MESSAGES TO THE CAPTAIN AND SENT THEM ON THEIR WAY. PUGWASH WAS VERY EXCITED!

This is too good to be true, me hearties! Here we are, stony broke, as usual...

... and there's a whopping great treasure, just round the corner, simply ASKING to be taken away!

BUT THE MATE, BARNABAS & WILLY WERE FAR FROM HAPPY.

Simply asking for TROUBLE you mean, Cap'n.

It's plain crazy, Cap'n! US... against all them big ships!

Aye... we'll be blown out of t'water by the lot of 'em!

IN THE MEANWHILE, THE PIGEONS
HAD REACHED THEIR DESTINATIONS.
ADMIRAL SIR SPLYCEMEIGH-MAINBRACE,
COMMANDER OF THE BRITISH FORCE,
WAS ENJOYING HIS USUAL BREAKFAST
OF ROAST BEEF AND BEER WHEN THE
MESSAGE ARRIVED.

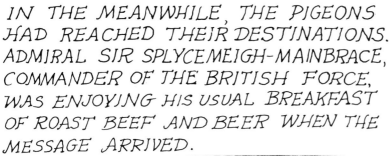

Bunkum Bay, eh!? Shiver me timbers... we must beat those dashed Frenchmen to it!

ANCHORS AWEIGH!!

AYE, AYE ADMIRAL SIR!

SQUAWK!

AND AT ONCE, BOTH NAVIES SAIL

AND ADMIRAL THE MARQUIS DE FRILLY DE POMMES-FRITES, IN CHARGE OF THE FRENCH FLEET, WAS TOYING WITH HIS EARLY MORNING BRANDY & CROISSANTS.

Hein! Ze Bay of Bunkum! Zose British blackguards shall not win ze day!

ALLONS, VITE - **VITE !!**

OUI - OUI, MON AMIRAL!

SQUAWK!

ORTH TOWARDS BUNKUM BAY...

MEANWHILE, JUST AS PUGWASH HAD EXPECTED, BOTH THE BRITISH AND FRENCH FLEETS HAD ARRIVED IN BUNKUM BAY AT THE VERY SAME HOUR...

...AND DREW UP OPPOSITE EACH OTHER AT THE ENTRANCE TO DO BATTLE.

AND... AS PUGWASH, TRUSSED UP & TERRIFIED, AWAITED THE END, JAKE HOISTED THE SPECIAL FLAG TO HIS MASTHEAD...

AND SET OUT FOR BUNKUM BAY.

BUT THE CAPTAIN HAD MADE ONE MISTAKE IN HIS CALCULATIONS...

THE SPECIAL FLAG *DIDN'T* TRAIL *BEHIND* THE SHIP AS JAKE THOUGHT IT WOULD,

IT BILLOWED OUT IN *FRONT* LIKE THE SAILS, BECAUSE TH[E] WIND WAS BLOWING THAT WA[Y]

SO THE BRITISH SAW WHAT THEY THOUGHT WAS A FRENCH SHIP SAILING B[Y] AND THE FRENCH SAW WHAT THEY TOOK TO BE A BRITISH SHIP LIKEWIS[E]

THE RESULTS WERE OBVIOUS!

SOON, ALL THE GUNS OF BOTH NAVIES HAD OPENED HEAVY FIRE ON THE LUCKLESS *Flying Dustman*...

SOON THE SHIP WAS REDUCED TO A SMOKING SINKING WRECK

FROM WHICH JAKE & HIS MEN WERE LUCKY TO ESCAPE ALIVE!

BUT, IN THE MEANWHILE, TIME WAS RUNNING OUT FOR THE CAPTAIN AND THE MATE AND BARNABAS AND WILLY.

AND THEN, JUST WHEN THE BIG BANG WAS DUE...

AND, STILL FIRING FURIOUSLY, BOTH FLEETS DRIFTED FAR AWAY. THE TWO ADMIRALS WERE TREMBLING WITH RAGE...

WHEREUPON BOTH WERE BLOWN FLAT ON THEIR BACKS...

AND QUITE FORGOT WHAT THE BATTLE WAS ABOUT ANYWAY.